GANESHA AND THE MOON

ONCE ON HIS BIRTHDAY, GANESHA WAS IN THE ABODE OF THE MOON, FOR A FEAST.

EVERYTHING IS SPLENDID BUT I LIKE THESE MODAKS* BEST.

WE HAD THEM MADE SPECIALLY FOR YOU, KNOWING THEY ARE YOUR FAVOURITE SWEET.

GANESHA ATE ALL THE MODAKS THAT WERE KEPT BEFORE HIM. VERY SOON –

I HAVE EATEN TOO MUCH. I FEEL SO UNCOMFORTABLE.

I NEED TO GET SOME FRESH AIR. I'LL GO FOR A RIDE ON MY MOUSE**.

*A SWEET DUMPLING FILLED WITH COCONUT AND JAGGERY
** THE MOUSE IS GANESHA'S 'VAHANA' OR STEED

1

IT WAS A BEAUTIFUL NIGHT. THE MOON SHONE SO BRIGHTLY, IT WAS ALMOST LIKE DAY!

SUDDENLY –

SQUEAK!

OH NO! ALL THE MODAKS I ATE HAVE FALLEN OUT.

PARDON ME, GANESHA. I DID NOT MEAN TO FRIGHTEN YOUR MOUSE.

THE MOON BURST OUT LAUGHING.

HA HA HA! YOU LOOK SO FUNNY! WHAT A FALL THAT WAS!

GANESHA WAS VERY ANGRY. BUT FIRST, HE PUT ALL THE MODAKS BACK...

HA HA HA!

... AND USED THE SNAKE TO TIE HIS STOMACH UP.

HO HO HO!

THE MOON JUST WOULD NOT STOP LAUGHING.

GANESHA BROKE OFF A PIECE OF HIS TUSK...

...AND HURLED IT , FURIOUSLY...

...SLASHING THE MOON'S LUMINOUS FACE.

O FOOLISH MOON! YOUR UNBLEMISHED APPEARANCE HAS MADE YOU VAIN! I COMMAND YOU TO VANISH FROM THE UNIVERSE!

THE MOON DISAPPEARED AND THERE WAS CHAOS IN HEAVEN AND ON EARTH.

OH! I CANNOT SEE ANYTHING.

WHAT HAS HAPPENED TO THE MOON?

IT IS SO DARK!

THE MOON WAS SORRY AND CAME TO GANESHA WITH THE OTHER GODS.

I HAVE LEARNED MY LESSON. I WILL NEVER MOCK YOU AGAIN.

TAKE BACK YOUR CURSE, O LORD! THE WORLD IS PLUNGED IN DARKNESS.

THE EVER-FORGIVING GANESHA THOUGHT FOR A WHILE. THEN –

YOU WERE WRONG TO LAUGH AT MY DISCOMFORT. I CANNOT TAKE BACK MY CURSE BUT I CAN SOFTEN IT.

THE MOON BOWED BEFORE GANESHA...

...AND WENT BACK TO HIS PLACE IN THE SKY.

*ALTERNATELY GROWING SMALLER AND LARGER

**PURNIMA OR POURNAMI
^AMAVASYA

GANESHA AND RAVANA

RAVANA, THE DEMON KING OF LANKA, OBSERVED SEVERE PENANCE TO PLEASE SHIVA.

OM NAMAH SHIVAYA!*

PLEASED WITH HIS AUSTERITIES, SHIVA APPEARED BEFORE HIM.

ASK FOR A BOON, RAVANA. I WILL GRANT YOU ANYTHING YOU WISH FOR.

LORD, I WANT THE ATMALINGA **.

* SALUTATIONS TO SHIVA
** THE ATMALINGA IS A FORM IN WHICH SHIVA IS WORSHIPPED.

SHIVA WAS DISMAYED.

THE ATMALINGA HAS THE POWER TO MAKE HIM INVINCIBLE. BUT I HAVE PROMISED TO GIVE HIM WHATEVER HE ASKS FOR.

YOU MUST WALK ALL THE WAY TO LANKA HOLDING THE ATMALINGA IN YOUR HANDS.

IT'S A LONG WAY FROM MOUNT KAILASH TO LANKA, BUT I CAN DO IT.

DON'T PUT THE ATMALINGA DOWN. IF YOU DO, EVEN FOR A MOMENT, IT WILL STAY ROOTED TO THAT SPOT FOR EVER.

AND THEN SHIVA DISAPPEARED.

RAVANA WAS JUBILANT.

NO ONE CAN EVER DESTROY ME! I HAVE ACQUIRED THE VERY POWER OF SHIVA!

RAVANA STARTED HIS JOURNEY BACK HOME, CAREFULLY CARRYING THE SACRED LINGA.

THE GODS WATCHED, AGHAST.

RAVANA IS OUR ENEMY AND A MENACE TO THE WORLD!

HE WILL DEFEAT US ALL!

WITH THE ATMALINGA, HIS POWER WILL BE GREATER THAN EVER!

THEY SOUGHT LORD GANESHA'S HELP.

O LORD! STOP RAVANA FROM TAKING THE ATMALINGA TO LANKA.

IF NOT, THE WORLD WILL BE IN MORTAL DANGER.

GANESHA THOUGHT FOR A WHILE.

HMMM... THAT IS NOT AN EASY TASK.

AND THEN –

DO NOT WORRY. I WILL FIND A WAY TO STOP RAVANA.

THE GODS WERE REASSURED.

VIGHNESHWARAYA NAMAHA!*

* SALUTATIONS TO YOU, O VIGHNESHWARA
VIGHNESHWARA – ONE WHO REMOVES OBSTACLES

8

GANESHA FOLLOWED RAVANA.

THERE HE IS! HE MUST NOT SEE ME.

RAVANA WALKED VERY FAST. HE SOON REACHED THE WEST COAST AND STRODE ALONG THE DESERTED SEA SHORE.

NOW IS MY CHANCE!

RAVANA IS A STICKLER FOR RITUALS. HE HAS TO PERFORM THE EVENING PRAYERS AT SUNSET EVERY DAY.

GANESHA INVOKED THE POWER OF LORD VISHNU TO BLOCK OUT THE SUN.

RAVANA WAS PUZZLED FOR A MOMENT.

STRANGE HOW THE SUN SET SO SUDDENLY!

BUT HE WAS UNSUSPECTING.

IT IS TIME FOR ME TO SAY MY EVENING PRAYERS.

AH, YOU CREATURE OF HABIT! THIS WILL CAUSE YOUR DEFEAT.

RAVANA FOUND HIMSELF IN A DILEMMA.

I CANNOT PUT THE LINGA DOWN AND I CANNOT PRAY WITH IT IN MY HANDS. I SHOULD ASK SOMEONE TO HOLD IT FOR ME.

HE LOOKED AROUND, WORRIED.

BUT THERE IS NO ONE HERE!

JUST THEN, HE SAW A YOUNG BRAHMIN BOY.

RAVANA IMMEDIATELY HELD OUT THE ATMALINGA.

HERE, BOY, HOLD THIS FOR ME.

THE BOY SHOOK HIS HEAD.

IT'S TOO HEAVY FOR ME. KEEP IT ON THE GROUND.

NO, I CAN'T! JUST HOLD IT TILL I FINISH MY PRAYERS.

IF IT IS TOO HEAVY FOR ME, CAN I PUT IT ON THE GROUND?

NO! NO!

THEN I CAN'T HOLD IT.

I WILL RETURN SOON. PLEASE HOLD IT TILL THEN.

WELL... ALL RIGHT.

RELIEVED, RAVANA HANDED OVER THE ATMALINGA.

THERE'S A GOOD BOY.

LITTLE DID HE KNOW THAT THE BOY WAS ACTUALLY GANESHA.

THE WILY GANESHA WAITED UNTIL RAVANA WAS IN THE MIDDLE OF HIS PRAYERS. THEN –

THIS IS TOO HEAVY FOR ME! I AM GOING TO PUT IT DOWN!

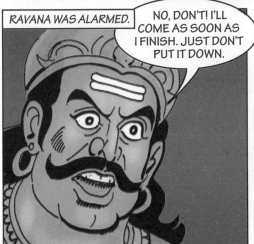

RAVANA WAS ALARMED.

NO, DON'T! I'LL COME AS SOON AS I FINISH. JUST DON'T PUT IT DOWN.

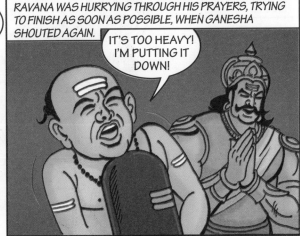

RAVANA WAS HURRYING THROUGH HIS PRAYERS, TRYING TO FINISH AS SOON AS POSSIBLE, WHEN GANESHA SHOUTED AGAIN.

IT'S TOO HEAVY! I'M PUTTING IT DOWN!

RAVANA FINISHED HIS PRAYERS IMMEDIATELY, AND RUSHED BACK, BUT IT WAS TOO LATE.

OH NO!

SUDDENLY, THE SUN WAS BACK IN THE SKY.

VISHNU HAD REMOVED THE ILLUSION

I HAVE BEEN TRICKED!

RAVANA TRIED TO MOVE THE LINGA.

IT WON'T BUDGE!

AN ENRAGED RAVANA CHASED THE BOY...

TAKE THAT, YOU RASCAL!

... AND HIT HIM THRICE ON HIS HEAD WITH HIS FISTS.

THEN GANESHA ASSUMED HIS TRUE FORM.

REALISING WHAT HE HAD DONE, RAVANA BOWED BEFORE GANESHA.

THE PLACE WHERE GANESHA PLACED THE ATMALINGA IS BELIEVED TO BE IN GOKARNA, KARNATAKA. THERE IS A TEMPLE BUILT AROUND THE ATMALINGA. NEXT TO IT IS A SHRINE OF GANESHA, WHERE THE IDOL HAS A DENT ON ITS FOREHEAD, SYMBOLISING THE INCIDENT.

THE TEMPLE OVER THE ATMALINGA IS CALLED THE MAHABALESHWAR TEMPLE. 'MAHABALA' MEANS GREAT POWER AND 'ISHWAR' MEANS GOD.

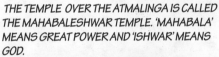

THE GREAT FORCE EXERTED BY RAVANA ON THE LINGA IS SAID TO HAVE CHANGED ITS SHAPE. THE LINGA NOW RESEMBLES THE EAR OF A COW. IN FACT, THE NAME GOKARNA, COMES FROM THIS. 'GO' - COW AND 'KARNAM' - EAR.

GANESHA RELEASES KAVERI

THE RIVER KAVERI IS OFTEN CALLED THE GANGA OF SOUTH INDIA. IT ORIGINATES IN THE BRAHMAGIRI HILLS IN COORG, IN A PLACE CALLED TALAKAVERI*. MANY STORIES ARE TOLD ABOUT HOW THE KAVERI CAME TO FLOW IN THIS REGION.

* POINT OF ORIGIN OF THE KAVERI

ONE SUCH STORY BEGINS AT THE WEDDING OF SHIVA AND PARVATI. IT WAS AN AUSPICIOUS OCCASION. ALL THE GODS, GODDESSES AND SAGES GATHERED AT MOUNT KAILASH, IN THE HIMALAYAS.

SUDDENLY, THE GROUND STARTED TO SINK.

OH!

AAAAAH!

HELP! HELP!

SHIVA CALMED EVERYONE DOWN AND THEN SUMMONED SAGE AGASTYA, ONE OF THE SAPTARISHIS*.

THE LAND, HERE IN THE NORTH, IS TILTING BECAUSE ALL OF US ARE GATHERED HERE. IF YOU TRAVEL SOUTH TO THE PODHIGAI HILLS **, YOU WILL ACT AS A COUNTER-BALANCE AND THE LANDS WILL BE STABLE.

O MAHESHWARA, I SHALL DO AS YOU SAY.

THEN SHIVA TOOK A FEW DROPS OF SACRED WATER FROM HIS MATTED LOCKS –

LET ME POUR THIS INTO YOUR WATER POT.

THE WATER POT NOW CONTAINS THE SACRED RIVER, KAVERI. FIND A SUITABLE SPOT IN THE MOUNTAINS TO SET IT DOWN. THE RIVER WILL THEN FLOW OUT IN WHICHEVER DIRECTION YOU POINT.

BIDDING FAREWELL, AGASTYA TRAVELLED SOUTH. ON THE WAY, HE VISITED MANY TEMPLES OF SHIVA.

* THE SEVEN SAGES WHO WERE BORN FROM BRAHMA'S MIND
** IN THE SOUTHERN PART OF THE WESTERN GHATS

TIME PASSED AND AGASTYA WANDERED IN THE SOUTHERN LANDS, LOOKING FOR THE PERFECT PLACE TO SET DOWN KAVERI. IN THE MEANTIME, INDRA, KING OF THE GODS, WAS ATTACKED BY A POWERFUL DEMON NAMED SURAPADMAN.

SURAPADMAN HAS THE UPPER HAND. I MUST ESCAPE.

INDRA FLED TO THE EARTH. HE STOPPED AT A PLACE CALLED SIRGAZHI, WHERE HE CREATED A MAGNIFICENT GARDEN.

I WILL PROPITIATE SHIVA WITH FLOWERS FROM MY GARDEN AND ASK HIM FOR HELP AGAINST THE WICKED SURAPADMAN.

BUT THERE WAS A TERRIBLE DROUGHT.

ALAS! THE FLOWERS IN MY GARDEN HAVE WILTED! HOW WILL I CONTINUE MY PRAYERS TO LORD SHIVA?

INDRA PLEADED WITH VARUNA, THE RAIN GOD.

O VARUNA, PLEASE BLOW SOME RAIN-BEARING CLOUDS HERE, SO THAT MY GARDEN CAN BLOOM AGAIN.

I CANNOT, INDRA. SURAPADMAN HAS THREATENED TO ATTACK ME IF I HELP YOU.

NARADA OVERHEARD THEM.

POOR INDRA! I MUST HELP HIM.

NARADA TOLD INDRA ABOUT AGASTYA'S WATER POT.

PRAY TO LORD GANESHA. HE WILL FIND A WAY TO HELP YOU.

I WILL DO AS YOU SAY, NARADA.

GANESHA ANSWERED INDRA'S PRAYERS.

YOUR GARDEN WILL GET WATER, INDRA.

HE TOOK THE FORM OF A CROW.

AGASTYA HAS THE RIVER KAVERI. I WILL FIND HIM AND END THE DROUGHT.

HE MUST BE SOMEWHERE HERE.

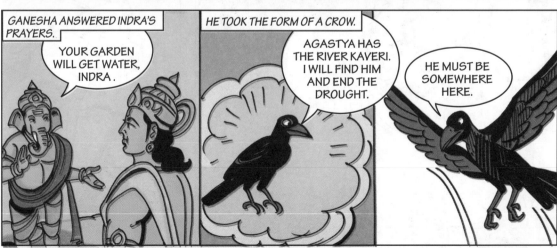

GANESHA SOON SPOTTED AGASTYA.

THERE HE IS!

HE FLEW DOWN AND PERCHED HIMSELF ON THE POT.

AGASTYA CHASED THE CROW AWAY.

SHOO! SHOO!

AS THE CROW FLEW OFF, THE POT FELL OVER.

INSIDE THE WATER POT, THE RIVER KAVERI MISINTERPRETED AGASTYA'S GESTURE…

…AND FLOWED OUT.

SUDDENLY, THE CROW TOOK THE FORM OF A SMALL BOY.

HUH?

PLAYING TRICKS ON ME? COME HERE!

AGASTYA CAUGHT THE BOY. HE WAS ABOUT TO RAP HIM ON THE HEAD WITH HIS KNUCKLES, WHEN THE BOY CHANGED HIS FORM.

LORD GANESHA!

O VIGHNESHWARA, FORGIVE ME! I ALMOST HIT YOU!

IN REPENTANCE, AGASTYA BEGAN STRIKING HIS FOREHEAD WITH HIS KNUCKLES.

STOP, AGASTYA...

...YOU ARE TRULY REPENTANT FOR A DEED YOU WERE ABOUT TO COMMIT UNKNOWINGLY. THIS IS A SIGN OF TRUE WISDOM.

THE DROUGHT WAS OVER. INDRA'S GARDEN FLOURISHED AGAIN. THE RIVER KAVERI STILL FLOWS ACROSS SOUTH INDIA.

GANESHA AND GANA

THE CHINTAMANI VINAYAKA TEMPLE AT THEUR IS ONE OF THE ASHTAVINAYAKA TEMPLES, THE EIGHT GANESHA TEMPLES NEAR PUNE. LIKE ALL THE OTHERS, THIS TEMPLE HAS ITS OWN STORY.

KING ABHISHEK AND HIS BEAUTIFUL QUEEN GUNAVATI, WERE FULL OF DESPAIR FOR THEY HAD NO CHILDREN. THEY WENT TO A SAGE FOR ADVICE.

HOW CAN WE GET AN HEIR, O WISE ONE?

DO NOT WORRY. PERFORM THE PENANCES I TELL YOU TO AND YOU WILL SURELY HAVE A SON.

JUST AS THE SAGE HAD PREDICTED—

OUR SON IS SO RADIANT!

WE SHALL CALL HIM GANA.

THE YOUNG PRINCE GREW UP TO BE A GREAT DEVOTEE OF SHIVA.

I AM PLEASED WITH YOUR DEVOTION, GANA. I WILL GRANT YOU SOME BOONS.

SHIVA'S BOONS MADE GANA POWERFUL AND ARROGANT.

ONE DAY, GANA AND HIS FRIENDS WENT HUNTING.

BUT THERE WAS NO SIGN OF A KILL FOR HOURS.

AFTER WANDERING FOR A WHILE, THEY REACHED THE ASHRAM OF SAGE KAPILA.

WELCOME, YOUNG PRINCE! YOU HONOUR ME WITH YOUR PRESENCE! PLEASE JOIN ME FOR A MEAL.

THIS IS THE CHINTAMANI GEM GIVEN TO ME BY LORD INDRA HIMSELF. IT HAS THE POWER TO GRANT ME WHATEVER I DESIRE.

SAGE KAPILA CLOSED HIS EYES AND CHANTED A FEW WORDS.

WHAT A WONDERFUL SPREAD!

SO MUCH FOOD!

AS HE ATE, GANA'S SELFISH MIND HAD BUT ONE THOUGHT.

I MUST HAVE THIS GEM.

AFTER THE MEAL -

THIS GEM IS WASTED HERE. LET ME TAKE IT TO MY PALACE WHERE IT WILL GET THE HONOUR DUE TO IT.

THANK YOU, BUT I PREFER TO KEEP IT WITH ME.

GANA FLEW INTO A RAGE.

THEN I SHALL TAKE IT AWAY FROM YOU.

AN ANGUISHED SAGE KAPILA PRAYED TO GANESHA FOR HELP.

PLEASE GET BACK THE CHINTAMANI, O GANESHA!

DO NOT WORRY. I SHALL RESTORE IT TO YOU.

GANESHA APPEARED IN GANA'S DREAM AND THREATENED HIM.

AAAARGH!

FAR FROM BEING FRIGHTENED, GANA GATHERED HIS ARMY FOR BATTLE.

DON'T FIGHT GANESHA, MY SON! REPENT WHILE YOU CAN.

OUT OF MY WAY, FATHER!

PUSHING HIS FATHER ASIDE, GANA THUNDERED TOWARDS SAGE KAPILA'S ASHRAM.

A FIERCE BATTLE ENSUED.

GANESHA KILLED GANA AND RETRIEVED THE GEM.

GANESHA IS KNOWN AS GANANAYAKA, MEANING 'ONE WHO DEFEATED GANA'.

BUT WHEN HE RETURNED THE GEM TO KAPILA –

O GANESHA! THIS GEM HAS BROUGHT NOTHING BUT MISERY. WILL YOU KEEP IT?

GANESHA AGREED TO DO SO.

YOU HAVE TAKEN A GREAT LOAD OFF MY MIND BY TAKING THE GEM!

SAGE KAPILA THEN INSTALLED AN IDOL OF GANESHA.

THIS FORM OF YOU, O BENEVOLENT LORD, SHALL BE CALLED CHINTAMANI VINAYAKA.

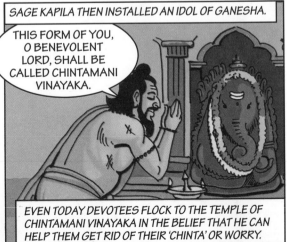

EVEN TODAY DEVOTEES FLOCK TO THE TEMPLE OF CHINTAMANI VINAYAKA IN THE BELIEF THAT HE CAN HELP THEM GET RID OF THEIR 'CHINTA' OR WORRY.

THE LEGEND OF SHAMI AND MANDAR

SAGE AURAVA WAS A LEARNED BRAHMIN, WHOSE FACE SHONE WITH THE RADIANCE OF KNOWLEDGE. TO HIM AND HIS WIFE WAS BORN A BEAUTIFUL DAUGHTER NAMED SHAMI.

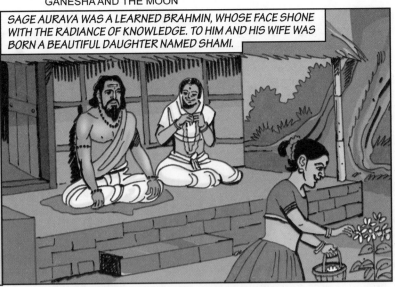

WHEN SHAMI WAS SEVEN YEARS OLD –

IT IS TIME WE GOT SHAMI MARRIED.

YES. WE SHALL WED HER TO MANDAR, SON OF RISHI DHAUMYA.

IN THOSE DAYS IT WAS THE CUSTOM TO GET SMALL CHILDREN MARRIED.

AFTER THE MARRIAGE CEREMONY –

ACCORDING TO OUR CUSTOM, YOU WILL BOTH CONTINUE TO STAY WITH YOUR PARENTS TILL YOU ARE OLDER.

AFTER SOME YEARS, MANDAR WENT TO SAGE AURAVA'S ASHRAM.

O SAGE! WITH YOUR PERMISSION I WILL TAKE SHAMI TO THE HOME OF MY GURU, SAGE SHAUNAK.

YOU HAVE MY BLESSINGS.

YOU MUST REACH YOUR DESTINATION BEFORE IT IS DARK, MY CHILDREN. TAKE THE SHORTER ROUTE WHICH GOES PAST THE ASHRAM OF SAGE BHRUSHUNDI.

BHRUSHUNDI HAD EARLIER BEEN A FISHERMAN WHO HAD TURNED TO THIEVING. ONCE, HE STOPPED THE RISHI MUGDALA TO ROB HIM.

HAND OVER YOUR BELONGINGS!

BUT THE SAGE DID NOT DO AS BHRUSHUNDI DEMANDED. INSTEAD –

AAH! WHAT IS THIS DAZZLING LIGHT THAT EMANATES FROM THE RISHI?

BHRUSHUNDI REALISED HE WAS IN THE PRESENCE OF A GREAT POWER AND ASKED FOR FORGIVENESS.

RISE, MY SON. PRAY TO LORD GANESHA AND YOUR PAST SINS WILL BE FORGIVEN.

BHRUSHUNDI TOOK THE SAGE'S ADVICE TO HEART AND STARTED WORSHIPPING GANESHA WITH SINGLE-MINDED DEVOTION.

GANESHA WAS VERY PLEASED AND BESTOWED A SINGULAR HONOUR ON HIM...

...AN ELEPHANT TRUNK GROWING FROM HIS FOREHEAD!

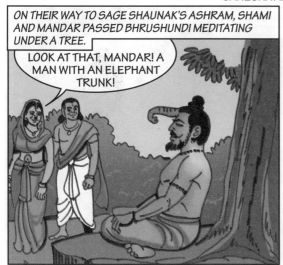

ON THEIR WAY TO SAGE SHAUNAK'S ASHRAM, SHAMI AND MANDAR PASSED BHRUSHUNDI MEDITATING UNDER A TREE.

LOOK AT THAT, MANDAR! A MAN WITH AN ELEPHANT TRUNK!

THE TWO BURST INTO UNCONTROLLABLE LAUGHTER.

I HAVE NEVER SEEN A FUNNIER SIGHT!

HA HA HA!

BHRUSHUNDI'S EYES FLEW OPEN. THEY BLAZED WITH ANGER.

WHO DARES LAUGH AT ME?

IN HIS RAGE, HE CURSED THE YOUNG COUPLE.

YOU WILL BECOME TREES! EVEN ANIMALS WILL TURN AWAY FROM YOU! NO BIRDS SHALL EAT THE LEAVES OF THE MANDAR* TREE OR REST ON THE THORNS OF THE SHAMI** TREE.

MANDAR! MY ARMS!

SHAMI! I CAN'T MOVE!

*THE INDIAN CORAL TREE
** INDIAN MESQUITE TREE

BHRUSHUNDI STORMED OFF, LEAVING THE BEAUTIFUL SHAMI AND HER HANDSOME HUSBAND, MANDAR, ROOTED TO THE SPOT AS TREES.

MEANWHILE GURU SHAUNAK WAITED ANXIOUSLY FOR SHAMI AND MANDAR.

WHY ARE THEY TAKING SO LONG TO COME?

AFTER A FEW DAYS, HE WENT TO SAGE AURAVA'S ASHRAM LOOKING FOR THEM.

BUT GURU SHAUNAK, OUR CHILDREN LEFT FOR YOUR ASHRAM DAYS AGO!

SOMETHING IS WRONG! LET US SET OUT AT ONCE TO LOOK FOR THEM.

AFTER DAYS OF SEARCHING THEY CAME TO BHRUSHUNDI'S ASHRAM WHERE THEY HEARD OF THE FATE THAT HAD BEFALLEN THEIR CHILDREN.

MY BELOVED SHAMI!

ALAS! MANDAR, MY DEAREST SON!

THE TWO FATHERS DECIDED TO APPEAL TO GANESHA FOR HELP AND BEGAN PRACTISING TERRIBLE AUSTERITIES.

AT LAST, GANESHA APPEARED BEFORE THEM IN AN IMPOSING FORM.

THEY BEGGED GANESHA TO RESTORE THEIR CHILDREN. BUT GANESHA WAS IN A DILEMMA.

I CANNOT DO THAT. IT WOULD DISPLEASE BHRUSHUNDI, MY GREAT DEVOTEE. BUT I CAN TEMPER HIS CURSE.

FINALLY –

I CANNOT BRING YOUR CHILDREN BACK TO LIFE BUT THEY WILL BE HONOURED IN THE THREE WORLDS. THE SHAMI AND MANDAR TREES WILL ALWAYS HAVE A SPECIAL IMPORTANCE ON EARTH.

GANESHA CONTINUED –

NO WORSHIP OF ME OR SHIVA WILL BE COMPLETE WITHOUT SHAMI LEAVES BEING PLACED ON THE ALTAR. SHIVA WILL BE PLEASED IF WORSHIPPED WITH THE FLOWERS OF THE MANDAR TREE.

THE 'PANCHANGA' OR FIVE PARTS OF THE SHAMI TREE, ITS ROOTS, FLOWERS, FRUITS, LEAVES AND BARK WILL HAVE MEDICINAL VALUE.

THE SHAMI TREE WILL BE WORSHIPPED ON THE FESTIVAL OF DUSSHERA. ITS SELF-KINDLING WOOD WILL BE CONSIDERED AUSPICIOUS FOR SACRIFICIAL PURPOSES.

THEN, GANESHA VANISHED. SAGE AURAVA WAS INCONSOLABLE WITH GRIEF.

UNABLE TO BEAR HIS SORROW HE BECAME THE FIRE WITHIN THE TRUNK OF THE SHAMI TREE.

AURAVA, MY FRIEND!

WHEN SACRIFICIAL FIRES ARE LIT, PRIESTS STILL RUB PIECES OF SHAMI WOOD TOGETHER AND THE HIDDEN FIRE LEAPS OUT.

TO THIS DAY, PEOPLE TIE STRIPS OF CLOTH ON THE SHAMI TREE AS AN OFFERING OR WHEN MAKING A VOW.

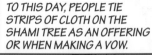

TRUE TO GANESHA'S WORDS, THE SHAMI AND MANDAR TREE REMAIN FOREVER AUSPICIOUS.